W9-BOM-350

LAUBACH WAY TO
Reading 2

A time-tested method that has taught millions of adults to read

MORE STORIES

New Readers Press
A Publishing Division of ProLiteracy

More Stories 2
ISBN 978-1-56420-930-6

Printed in the United States of America
9 8 7 6 5 4 3 2 1

All proceeds from the sale of New Readers Press materials
support literacy programs in the United States and worldwide.

Developmental Editor: Terrie Lipke
Creative Director: Andrea Woodbury
Production Specialist: Maryellen Casey
Art and Design Supervisor: James P. Wallace
Illustrations: Luigi Galante, represented by Wilkinson Studios, Inc.
Cover Design: Carolyn Wallace

To the Teacher

More Stories 2 is a supplementary reader for *Laubach Way to Reading 2*. It contains three stories correlated to the new words in each lesson of skill book 2.

If a student needs extra reading practice, you may help him read these stories in class. If a student is able to read independently, he may enjoy and benefit from reading these stories at home.

Great care has been taken to make sure that each story in this book corresponds to its skill book lesson. The new words in each lesson are reinforced in the three stories for that lesson. The stories for Lesson 14 include words from the first two chapters in the correlated reader *City Living*, which are read as part of Lesson 14. The stories for Lesson 15 include words from all of the five remaining chapters in *City Living*, so the Lesson 15 stories should be read after *City Living* is completed.

The vocabulary in *More Stories 2* has been carefully controlled. Most of the new words have short vowel sounds, although a few highly useful sight words with long vowel sounds are introduced.

Any new words in a story are listed at the beginning of that story. You should go over the new words with the student before having him read the story. Have the student sound out the new words with short vowel sounds. Tell him the sight words, and have him repeat them after you.

This book may be used not only with English-speaking students, but also with speakers of other languages who are learning English. New vocabulary words are listed at the back of the book with suggestions for teaching. No new grammatical structures are used.

Contents

At the Gift Shop

your

This is Miss Pam York.
This is Miss Kim York.
Kim is Pam's little sister.

This is Mrs. York.
Pam and Kim are her children.

The telephone rings.
Kim picks up the telephone.
She yells, "Pam!"
Kim yells, "Mr. Glenn is on the telephone.
He is the man at the gift shop."

Kim gives the telephone to Pam.

Pam picks up the telephone.
She says, "This is Pam York."

Mr. Glenn tells Pam, "Your gift is at the shop.
Your gift for Mrs. York is at the shop."

* * *

Pam and Kim are at the gift shop.
Mrs. York is at the gift shop.

Mr. Glenn gives a box to Pam.
Pam looks in the box.
Three rings are in the box.

Pam gives the box to Mrs. York.
Pam tells Mrs. York, "This is your gift.
One ring is for you."

Mrs. York puts a ring on her finger.
She says, "This ring is big for my finger."
She puts the big ring in the box.

Mrs. York puts a ring on her finger.
She says, "This ring is little for my finger."
She puts the little ring in the box.

Mrs. York puts a ring on her finger.
She says, "This ring is not big.
It is not little.
This is my gift."

Mrs. York thanks the girls.
The girls thank Mr. Glenn.

A Gift for Miss Hill

class	me

Bob is at a gift shop.
He is getting a gift for Miss Hill.

Bob is in Miss Hill's class.
The class is giving a gift to Miss Hill.
Bob is getting the gift.

Bob looks at a big dish.
He looks at little cups.
He looks at an Indian ring.

Bob puts the Indian ring on his finger.
The ring is big.
Bob says to the woman in the shop,
    "The ring is not for me.
It is for Miss Hill.
Miss Hill's finger is little.
Do you have a little Indian ring?"

The woman gets a little Indian ring.
She sells the ring to Bob.

Bob puts the little ring in a big box.
In class, he tells the boys and girls,
    "Look at this big box.
The gift for Miss Hill is in this big box."

The boys and girls look at the big box.
They say, "Is the gift big?"

Bob says, "No, it is a little gift in a big box.
The gift is an Indian ring."

The boys and girls put their names on the box.
They give their gift to Miss Hill.
They yell, "This is for you, Miss Hill!"

Miss Hill says, "Is this big box for me?"
She looks in the big box.
She picks up the little ring.

Miss Hill says, "An Indian ring!
Is this for me?"
Miss Hill puts the ring on her finger.
She thanks the class for the gift.

Sisters

Ann Roberts is 32.
Ann has five sisters.

Ann's sister Fran is 30.
Ann's sister Jill is 28.
Ann's sister Kim is 23.
Ann's sister Liz is 19.
Ann's sister Pam is 16.

Ann Roberts is the big sister.
Pam Roberts is the little sister.

Mr. and Mrs. Roberts have six children.
They have six girls.

Dinner in the Kitchen

having

Mr. and Mrs. Glenn have two children.
Their children are Ann and Bob.
The children have a bird and a pup.

The Glenns are sitting in the kitchen.
They are having dinner.
They are having fish for dinner.

The bird is in the kitchen.
The bird is singing.
Ann is singing with the bird.

Mr. Glenn tells Ann, "Not at dinner!"

Bob whistles for the little pup.
The pup runs into the kitchen.
The pup jumps on Bob's leg.
Bob gives a little of the fish to the pup.

Mrs. Glenn tells Bob, "Not at dinner!"

The Glenns are having dinner.
Ann is not singing with the bird.
Bob is not giving fish to the pup.

Ed's Whistle

Ed Hill is in the kitchen.
He has a little whistle.
Ed whistles with his whistle.

Jill is Ed's sister.
She is in the kitchen with Ed.
She is looking at his whistle.

Bob Oliver yells, "Ed! I am in the street.
Look! I am jumping!"

Ed runs to the street.
He jumps with Bob.
The two boys jump and jump.

Ed tells Bob, "I have a whistle."
Ed runs to the kitchen for his whistle.
The whistle is not in the kitchen.

Ed looks at Jill.
"Do you have my whistle?" he says.

Jill says, "No."

Ed yells at Jill, "You have my whistle!
Give it to me!
It is not your whistle!
It is my whistle!"

Bob Oliver is in the street.
He yells, "Ed! Your whistle is in the street!"

Ed runs to the street and gets his whistle.
He thanks Bob.
Ed runs to the kitchen.
He looks at Jill.
He tells her, "I am giving my whistle to you."

Jill says, "Thank you, Ed."
She whistles with Ed's little whistle.

Fish for Dinner

The Hills are at the river.
Mr. Hill is fishing in the river.
The children are with him.
They are fishing with him.

The Hills' tent is at the river.
Mrs. Hill is in the tent.

The children run to the tent.
Ed yells, "I am bringing a big fish!"
Jill yells, "I am bringing two big fish!"
Kim yells, "I am bringing three big fish!"

Mrs. Hill looks at the fish.
She whistles.
She tells the children, "They are big fish!"

The Hills have the fish for dinner.
The Hills' dinner is six big fish.

A Lily for Kitty

Jimmy Fisher lives in a city.
It is a windy city.

Jimmy lives with his sister Pam.
Jimmy and Pam live in a big building.
Their building is at 15 Hill Street.

Kitty King is visiting Pam Fisher.
Pam and Kitty are sitting in the kitchen.

Jimmy runs in.
He is bringing a pretty lily.
It is a gift for his sister.

Pam tells Kitty,
    "Kitty, this is Jimmy.
I am Jimmy's big sister.
Jimmy lives with me."

Pam tells Jimmy,
    "Jimmy, this is Kitty.
Kitty lives on this street.
She lives at 16 Hill Street."

Jimmy looks at Kitty.
She is pretty.
Jimmy's sister does not get the lily.
Jimmy gives the lily to Kitty.

Jimmy and Kitty

Jimmy Fisher has Kitty King's picture.
Jimmy looks at Kitty's picture.
He is singing.
He is looking at the picture and singing.

Jimmy is going to a gift shop.
His sister sells rings in the shop.
He tells his sister, "I am looking for a ring.
I am getting a ring for Kitty."

His sister gets six pretty rings.
Jimmy looks at the rings.

His sister tells him, "This is a pretty ring."
She puts it on her finger.
Jimmy looks at the ring on her finger.

His sister gives the ring to Jimmy.
He looks at the ring.
He tells his sister, "It is a pretty ring.
I am getting this ring for Kitty."
His sister sells the ring to him.

*   *   *

Jimmy is visiting Kitty.
He tells her, "I have a ring for you, Kitty."
He gives the pretty ring to Kitty.
He puts it on her finger.

Kitty looks at the ring on her finger.
She looks at Jimmy.
She puts her hand in his hand.
She says, "Thank you for the pretty ring, Jimmy."

18   Lesson 3, Story 3

Fran Visits the Big City

go	thing

Kitty King lives in a big city.
Her sister Fran lives in a little city.
Fran is visiting Kitty in the big city.

Fran and Kitty go to shops.
They look at things in the shops.
Fran looks at things in the streets.
She looks at the big buildings.

Fran and Kitty go to York Street.
They go to a big building on York Street.
They go to little shops in this big building.
They look at things in the shops.

Fran and Kitty go to River Street.
They go to a big building on River Street.
They look at pictures in this building.

Fran and Kitty go to the river.
They look at the river.
It is windy at the river.

Fran says, "This is a pretty city.
It has big buildings.
It has a pretty river.
It has pretty things in the shops."

A Duck Dinner

Mr. Hill is at Mud River.
His son Ed is with him.

Mr. Hill has his gun with him.
Ed has his gun with him.
Mr. Hill and his son are hunting ducks.
Ducks are at Mud River.

The sun is up.
Ed is looking at the sun.

Mr. Hill is looking at the ducks.
He yells to his son, "Look! Six ducks!
Hit the ducks, son!"

Ed hits one duck.
Mr. Hill hits two ducks.

"Get the ducks," Mr. Hill tells his son.
"Bring the ducks to the tent."

Ed brings the ducks to the tent.
One duck is big.
Two ducks are little.
"You hit the big duck," Mr. Hill tells Ed.

"Cut up the ducks," Mr. Hill tells his son.
Ed cuts up the ducks.

Mr. and Mrs. Glenn are at the river.
They do not have a duck.
Mr. Hill looks at the Glenns.

"Give a duck to the Glenns," he tells Ed.

Ed tells Mr. Glenn,
    "We have three ducks.
One duck is for you.
Have a duck dinner!"
Ed gives the big duck to Mr. Glenn.

Mr. Hill and his son have a duck dinner.
They have two little ducks for dinner.
Mr. and Mrs. Glenn have a duck dinner.
They have a big duck for dinner.

Pam York and Her Sons

Pam York lives in a city.
She lives in a big building.
Her two little sons live with her.

Pam gets up at six.
She has two eggs.
She sits in the kitchen.
She looks at the city buildings.
The city is pretty at six.
The sun is up.
It is not windy.

Pam's sons get up at seven.
They have two eggs.
Her sons do not sit and look at the city.
They run and yell in the kitchen.
They bring mud in the kitchen.
They cut up Pam's pictures.

Pam yells at her sons.
"Do not run and yell in the kitchen!
Do not cut up my pictures!
Pick up the mud!"

Pam's sons pick up the mud.
They whistle and sing.

The Pup Tent

Mr. Hill is in Sam's shop.
Sam's shop is in the city.
The shop is in a big building.

Mr. Hill is looking for a pup tent.
A pup tent is a little tent.
Mr. Hill is getting a pup tent for his son.
He is getting the tent for his son Ed.

Mr. Hill tells Sam, "I am looking for a pup tent.
The pup tent is for my son."

Sam sells a little pup tent to Mr. Hill.
Sam puts it in a box.
Mr. Hill thanks Sam.

Mr. Hill whistles.
He has a gift for his son Ed.

Ann Gets Stuck

| Hunt | coming | out |

Ann Hunt lives in the valley.
She lives with her mother and little brother.
Ann's mother has a shop in the valley.

Ann has a truck.
She brings things from the city in her truck.
She brings things from the city to the valley.
Ann's mother sells the things in her shop.

Ann is coming from the city in her truck.
She has bricks in her truck.
She has two tents in her truck.
She has a box of cups in her truck.
She has a box of pans in her truck.

Ann comes to some mud.
Her truck gets stuck in the mud.
Ann gets some bricks out of the truck.
She puts the bricks in the mud.
She gets the truck out of the mud.

Ann's little brother Bud yells, "Mother!
A truck is coming!
Ann's truck is coming!"

Ann gets out of the truck.
Her little brother looks at her.
Bud says, "You have mud on your hands.
You have mud on your neck.
You have mud on your legs.
You do not look pretty, Ann!"
Bud thinks this is funny.

Ann's mother does not think it is funny.
"Ann, are you hurt?" she says.

Ann says, "No, I am not hurt.
Mud does not hurt me.
And my brother's words do not hurt me."

The Pup Brings the Ducks

Jimmy Oliver is going hunting.
He is going hunting with his brother Bob.
Jimmy and Bob are going hunting for ducks.

Jimmy brings his pup with him.
Bob thinks this is funny. He says,
  "Are you bringing this little pup to hunt?
This little thing does not hunt ducks!"

Jimmy tells his brother,
  "Yes, I am bringing my pup to hunt.
This little pup does hunt ducks."

At the river, Jimmy hits a duck.
He hits the duck in the wing.
The duck is in the mud.

Jimmy yells to his pup,
  "Get the duck!"

The pup gets the duck from the mud.
Jimmy yells to his pup,
  "Come! Come!"
The pup brings the duck to Jimmy.
Jimmy pets the pup.

Lesson 5, Story 2

Bob hits a duck.
The pup gets the duck from the river.
Bob yells to his brother's pup,
    "Come! Come!"
The pup brings the duck to Bob.
Bob pets the pup.

The brothers put the ducks in their trucks.
The little pup gets in the truck.

Bob pets his brother's pup.
He tells Jimmy,
    "Your pup does hunt ducks."

The Zipper Is Stuck

dress	6:30	6:15

Pam is having dinner with Bud.
Bud is coming to get Pam at 6:30.

It is 6:15.
Pam is putting on her dress.

Pam yells, "Mother! Mother!
Come! Come!
My zipper is stuck.
The zipper on my dress is stuck.
It is 6:15.
Bud is coming at 6:30."

Pam's mother runs in.
She looks at the dress.
She looks at the zipper.
She tells Pam, "It is stuck!"

Pam's zipper is stuck.
Pam's mother thinks it is funny.
Pam does not think it is funny.

Pam's mother gets the zipper up.

Bud comes at 6:30.

Giving Help

Fred Roberts is twelve.
Liz Roberts is seven.
Fred and Liz live at 15 Hill Street.

Ellen Fisher lives at 17 Hill Street.
Miss Fisher is seventy.

Fred and Liz Roberts help Miss Fisher.
They help her with many things.
They go to the shop for her.
They get fresh eggs.
They get fresh fish.
They help Miss Fisher in the kitchen.

Miss Fisher helps the children.
She helps Fred and Liz with their lessons.

Ellen Sells Eggs

fifty

Ellen Bell lives in the valley.
Ellen has many hens.
She has seventy big hens.
She has twelve little hens.

Ellen gets many eggs from her hens.
She gets big eggs from the big hens.
She gets little eggs from the little hens.

The hens sit on their nests.
Ellen picks up the eggs from the nests.

The eggs are very fresh.
Ellen sells the fresh eggs.
She sells twelve big eggs for seventy cents.
She sells twelve little eggs for fifty cents.

Ed Oliver comes to the valley.
He looks at Ellen's eggs.
Ellen says, "The big eggs are seventy cents.
The little eggs are fifty cents."

Ed says, "I will get twelve of the little eggs."
He gives fifty cents to Ellen.
Ellen gives a box of twelve little eggs to Ed.

30   Lesson 6, Story 2

Ed says, "Do you sell your hens?"

Ellen says, "I sell some of my big hens.
Some of the big hens do not give eggs.
I do not sell my little hens.
They give eggs.
And I do not have many little hens."

Ed says, "I will get one of your big hens."
Ellen sells a big hen to Ed.
Ed thanks Ellen for the eggs and the hen.

Uncle Ted Hits a Hen

we	OK

Glenn Hill and his uncle are hunting ducks.
The men are hunting ducks at the river.

Glenn Hill has his gun.
He hits a duck!
He hits two ducks!

Many ducks are at the river.
Two hens are at the river.
The hens are with the ducks.

Uncle Ted looks at the ducks.
He has his gun.
He does not hit a duck.
He hits a hen!

Uncle Ted looks at the hen.
"I hit a hen!" he yells.

Glenn Hill runs to Uncle Ted.
Glenn picks up the hen.
He says, "This is Ellen Bell's hen.
You hit one of her hens.
We will tell her."

The men bring the hen to Ellen Bell.
Uncle Ted says, "I hit one of your hens.
We have two ducks.
We will give you the two ducks for your hen."

Ellen Bell says, "OK. Two ducks are OK."

Uncle Ted gives Ms. Bell the two ducks.
He tells Ms. Bell, "Thanks.
I will not hit your hens.
I will look.
I will hit ducks."

Sick in Bed

Ned is sick in bed.

Two men come to visit Ned.
The men are his uncles.
One man is Uncle Bob.
One man is Uncle Cal.

Ned's uncles bring a big box.
They put the box on Ned's bed.

Ned looks in the box.
A little red truck is in the box.
Ned thanks his uncles for their gift.
They tell him, "Get well quickly!"
Ned visits with his uncles, and they go.

Two women come to visit Ned.
The women are his mother's friends.
One woman is Mrs. Bell.
One woman is Miss Fisher.

The women bring some apples to Ned.
They tell him, "Get well quickly!"
Ned thanks the women for their gift.
He visits with them, and they go.

Ned's mother comes in and sits on his bed.
She says, "I have a letter for you."
The letter is from Ned's class.
It says, "Get well quickly!"

Ned says, "I will send a letter to my class.
I will thank them for this letter.
I will send a letter to your friends, Mother.
I will thank them for the apples.
I will send a letter to my uncles.
I will thank them for the little red truck."

Lesson 7, Story 1   35

Big Man Jimmy

Kitty's telephone rings.
Jimmy Fisher is on the telephone.
Kitty says, "Come to dinner, Jimmy."

Jimmy says, "Thanks, Kitty.
I will bring a hen for dinner.
I will come at four."

Kitty says, "My sister Fran is visiting me.
Fran and I will get dinner."

It is four.
Jimmy brings the hen.
Kitty says, "Bring the hen to the kitchen.
Fran is not well.
Will you help me in the kitchen, Jimmy?"

Jimmy says, "I will not help you in the kitchen.
Men do not help in the kitchen."

Kitty yells, "Jimmy!
You think you are a big man.
A big man helps his mother.
A big man helps his sister.
A big man helps his girl friend!"

Jimmy yells, "I will not help in the kitchen!"

Kitty yells, "You think you are a big man!
I think you are a very little man!"
Jimmy runs from the kitchen.
He runs to the street.

* * *

Jimmy is in his building.
He looks at his clock.
It is seven.

Jimmy thinks and thinks.
"A big man does help women," he thinks.
"I will tell Kitty."

Jimmy picks up the telephone.
"Kitty, this is Jimmy," he says.

Kitty says, "Yes?"

Jimmy says, "Kitty, listen to me.
A man helps his woman."

Kitty says, "You are a big man, Jimmy.
Will you come to dinner?
Fran is well.
She will help me in the kitchen."

Jimmy says, "Fran and I will help you.
We will help you in the kitchen."

A Letter for Ellen

when	doing

Ellen Bell has two sons.
One son lives with her.
One son does not.

Ellen's son Ted lives with her.
He is 15.
Ted helps Ellen on her farm.

Ellen's son Fred does not live with her.
Fred is 18.
Fred lives in a big city.
Fred is going to class in the city.

Ellen sends many letters to Fred.
She does not get many letters from him.

In her letters, Ellen says,
   "Are you sick?
Are you well?
Do you have many friends?
Are you doing well in your class?
When will you come to visit me?
When will you send a letter to me?
When will you send a picture of you?"

Ellen sends ten letters to her son Fred.
She gets one letter from him.

In his letter, Fred says,
    "No.
Yes.
Yes.
Yes.
Quickly.
Quickly.
Quickly."

The Hunts' Cat Gets Two Dinners

Hunts'	had

The Hunt family is in the kitchen.
Kim is the Hunts' little girl.
She is two.
Kim is having her dinner.
Mrs. Hunt is getting dinner for Mr. Hunt.
Mr. Hunt is standing with his back to Kim.

The Hunts' black cat comes in.
He is standing in the kitchen.
The cat looks at Kim.
He looks at her dinner.

Kim looks at the cat.
She picks up some of her dinner.
She picks it up in her hands.
She gives some of her dinner to the cat.

Mr. Hunt looks at Kim.
Kim is giving her dinner to the cat.
Mr. Hunt says, "Kim!
That is your dinner.
That is not the cat's dinner."

40   Lesson 8, Story 1

Kim's mother looks up.
She says to the cat,
    "You cannot have Kim's dinner.
This is your dinner."
She puts the cat's dinner in a dish.

Mr. Hunt picks up Kim.
He says, "Kim, you are a funny girl.
You give your dinner to the cat."

Mrs. Hunt says to the cat,
    "You had two dinners.
You had your dinner.
And you had Kim's."

Will Jack and Fran Marry?

Jack Oliver will marry Fran King.
Jack has a black cat.
Fran cannot live with a cat.
She gets sick from cats.

Fran says to Jack,
    "I cannot live with a cat.
Give your cat to a friend."

Jack says, "I cannot do that.
My cat kills rats for me.
My cat is my friend."

Fran says, "I cannot marry you and your cat!"

Jack says, "OK. I will give my cat to a friend.
I can give my cat to Sam Smith."
Jack picks up his cat.
He puts his cat in a basket.

Jack is carrying his cat in a basket.
He is carrying his cat to Sam Smith.
The cat will live with the Smith family.

Jack runs back to Fran.
Fran says, "I will marry you, Jack!"
Jack and Fran are very happy.

Hunting with Ed and Cal

did	dead (ded)

Cal and Ed are hunting.
Ed kills a duck.
He brings the duck to Cal's truck.
Cal is not at the truck.

Ed is standing at the truck.
Cal does not come.
Ed sits.
Cal does not come.

Ed thinks, "A man is hunting at the river.
The man is hunting ducks with his gun.
Did he kill Cal?
Is Cal dead?"

Ed looks for Cal.
He thinks, "Is Cal hurt?
Is Cal dead?
Did that man hit him with his gun?"

Cal does not come.
Ed looks and looks.
He listens and listens.
He yells, "Cal! Cal!"

44   Lesson 8, Story 3

Ed listens.
He yells, "Cal! Yell to me!"

Cal yells, "Help! Come quickly!
I am hurt, Ed! I hurt my leg!
I cannot stand up!
Quick, come to me!"

Ed yells, "Are you at the river?"
Cal yells, "Yes, I am!"

Ed runs to the river.
He comes to Cal.
Cal's leg is hurt.
Cal cannot get up.
Ed helps Cal to the truck.

Cal is not dead.
Ed gives thanks.

Fran King and Jack Oliver Marry

marrying	our

The Oliver family is visiting the King family.
Jack Oliver is marrying Fran King.

Many gifts are in the kitchen.
Kitty King puts a gift in the kitchen.
Kitty is Fran's sister.
Her gift is a pretty glass dish.

Mrs. King puts a gift in the kitchen.
Her gift is some cups and pans.
Mr. King puts a gift in the kitchen.
His gift is a tent.

Mr. and Mrs. Oliver bring a big gift.
They do not put their gift in the kitchen.
Their gift is a red truck.
They put it in back of the building.

After they marry, Fran and Jack look at their gifts.
They are happy!
They laugh and laugh!

Fran tells her sister, "Thanks, Kitty.
Thank you for our pretty dish."

Fran tells her mother, "Thanks, Mother.
Thank you for our cups and pans."

Jack tells Mr. King, "Thank you.
Thank you for our tent."

Jack tells his mother and father, "Thanks.
Thank you for our truck."

After lunch, Fran and Jack get in their truck.
They put their gifts in their truck.
They tell their family,
    "We will go to the valley.
We will live in our tent at the river."

Fran and Jack visit the valley.
They live in their tent at the river.
They have a happy visit in the valley.

After their visit in the valley,
    Fran and Jack will come back to the city.
They will live in a big brick building.
Fran and Jack are very happy!

Going to Class with Friends

bus

Sam Smith comes to class at seven.
He comes on the bus.

Fran Roberts comes to class at seven.
She comes on the bus.
Fran sits with Sam on the bus.

Sam and Fran are friends.
The two friends go to class.

At twelve, the bell rings.
The boys and girls in the class go to lunch.

Fran and Sam sit in the back of the building.
They sit on the grass.

Fran has her lunch with her.
Sam did not bring his lunch.
Fran gives half of her lunch to Sam.
She gives half of her apple to Sam.

Many friends sit with Fran and Sam.
They sit on the grass and have lunch.
Fran, Sam, and their friends are happy.
They laugh and laugh.

After lunch, the boys and girls go up the path.
They go back to class in the building.
In class, they do not laugh.
They study their lessons.

At three, the bell rings.
The boys and girls go out of the building.
After class, Fran and Sam run on the grass.
They run and laugh with their friends.

The Man on the Path

bad

Jack King gets in bed at ten.
He thinks of his factory.
It is a glass factory.

Mr. King thinks and thinks.
It is eleven.

Mr. King thinks, "I will get up.
I will write some letters at the factory.
The men and women are not at the factory.
I can write many letters."

* * *

Jack King is coming to his factory.
He is coming up the path.
The path runs from the river to the factory.

Some glass is on the path.
Some glass is on the grass.
Mr. King looks at the glass.
"That is funny," he thinks.

Mr. King looks up the path.
A man is standing at the factory.
He is standing on the path.
Mr. King thinks, "That is funny.
It is twelve.
The men and women are not at the factory."

Jack King stands on the path.
He thinks,
  "Is that a bad man?
Is he coming from the factory?
Did he get some things from the factory?"

Jack thinks,
  "That man has a bag in his hand.
Is he carrying a gun in the bag?"

"No, it is not a bag," Jack King thinks.
"It is a bat.
It is a big bat.
That man is carrying a big bat!
He is a bad man!"

Jack King thinks,
  "Some glass is on the path.
Does that bad man have some glass?
Does he have some glass in his hand?
He can cut me with the glass."

"Will he cut me with the glass?
Will he hit me with the bat?" he thinks.

Jack King thinks,
  "I will run to the street.
I will run to the telephone up the street.
I will run quickly.
That bad man cannot get me!"

*   *   *

Jack King is running.
He is running from the factory.
The man is running after Jack King.

The man is yelling.
"Jack! Jack! Come back! Come back!
I am your friend, Bob Hunt!"

Jack King looks at the man.
It is his friend!

Bob Hunt is carrying a basket.
Bob says, "I am coming from the valley.
I am bringing some apples from the valley.
Half of them are for you."

Jack King laughs and laughs.

Molly Is Sick

pill

Molly's head is hot.
Molly looks for her mother.

Mrs. Roberts looks at Molly.
She puts her hand on Molly's head.
She says, "You are sick, Molly."

Mrs. Roberts runs to the telephone.
She telephones Dr. Chan.
The doctor picks up the telephone.
The doctor listens to Mrs. Roberts.
The doctor says, "Bring Molly to my office."

Mrs. Roberts brings Molly to the doctor's office.
She writes her name and address for the doctor.

Dr. Chan looks at Molly.
She says, "Mrs. Roberts, Molly is sick.
Put her to bed.
I have some pills for her.
The pills will help her get well.
Give her one pill after lunch.
Give her one pill after dinner."

Dr. Chan gives the pills to Mrs. Roberts.
Mrs. Roberts thanks the doctor.

Mrs. Roberts puts Molly to bed.
After lunch, she gives one pill to Molly.
After dinner, she gives one pill to Molly.

Molly gets well.
The pills help Molly get well.

Lesson 10, Story 1   55

Tom's Job

Tom Roberts can fix many things.
He can fix many little things.
He can fix locks.
He can fix clocks.
He can fix dolls.

Tom Roberts got a job.
He got a job in a fix-it shop.

Don Smith brings a clock to the fix-it shop.
"Can you fix this clock?" he says to Tom.
"I dropped the clock, and it stopped."

Tom looks at the clock.
"Yes, I can fix it," he says.
"It is a little job.
Come back at four."

Molly Hunt comes to the fix-it shop.
She is carrying a doll.
The doll's head is in her hand.

"Can you fix this doll?" Molly says to Tom.
"It is my little girl's doll.
Her brother hit it with a rock."

Tom looks at the doll.
Tom says, "Yes, I can fix the doll.
I can put the head back on the doll.
Come back at five."

Don Smith comes back to the fix-it shop at four.
Tom gives him the clock.
Mr. Smith gives six dollars to Tom.

Mrs. Hunt comes back to the fix-it shop at five.
Tom gives the doll to her.
Mrs. Hunt gives two dollars to Tom.
She says to Tom, "You fix things very well."

A Factory Job

front (frunt)

John Smith has a job.
John has a job at a bat factory.
The bat factory is in a big building.

The factory is not in the city.
It is in the valley.
John lives in the city.
He lives in a big building in the city.

John gets up at five.
He has two eggs.
He gets on the bus at six.
The bus stops in front of the bat factory.
John comes to the factory at seven.

A big whistle is on top of the factory.
It whistles at twelve.
The men and women stop for lunch.
Some of them have lunch in back of the factory.
They sit on the grass.

One of the men says funny things at lunch.
The men and women laugh.
This man's name is Robert Bell.
Robert and John are friends.

58   Lesson 10, Story 3

The whistle on top of the factory whistles at one.
The men and women go back to their jobs.

After lunch, a doctor comes to the factory.
He is standing in the office.
The office is in the front of the building.
The men and women go to the office.

The doctor gives shots to the men and women.
He tells them, "You cut your hands on the job.
The shots will help you.
You will not get sick from the cuts."

John gets out of the factory at four.
He gets on the bus.
The bus stops in front of his building at five.

John has dinner.
After dinner, he visits his friends.

The Glass Factory Burns

jumped	helped

Mr. Glenn was sitting in his kitchen.
His son John was sitting with him.

A man ran in.
He yelled, "The glass factory is burning!
Come quickly and help stop it from burning!"

Then they heard the factory whistle.
Mr. Glenn and John jumped up.
The three men ran to the glass factory.
The big building was burning.

Some men in a red truck heard the factory
    whistle.
They hurried to the factory in the truck.
The men jumped from the truck.
They ran to the building.
They stopped the factory from burning.
Mr. Glenn and John helped them.

Mr. Glenn hurried back to the kitchen.
John hurried back to the kitchen.

Robert Gets a Cast on His Leg

cast

Robert Oliver was running in the street.
He hurt his leg.
Robert yelled to his father, "Help!
My leg is hurt! I cannot stand up!"

Mr. Oliver hurried to Robert.
He looked at Robert's leg.
He yelled to Mrs. Oliver, "Robert's leg is hurt!"

Mrs. Oliver ran to telephone Dr. Fisher.
Mrs. Oliver said, "Dr. Fisher!
Our son hurt his leg!
He cannot stand up!"

Dr. Fisher said, "Bring him to my office."

The Olivers hurried to the doctor's office.
Mr. Oliver helped Robert.

First, Miss Bird looked at Robert's leg.
Miss Bird was Dr. Fisher's nurse.
Then the doctor looked at Robert's leg.

The doctor said, "I will fix your leg quickly.
First, I will cover your leg.
Then, I will put a cast on it.
Your leg will not hurt with the cast on it."

Dr. Fisher covered Robert's leg.
Then he put the cast on it.
The nurse helped the doctor.

Then, Dr. Fisher said, "Your leg will get well.
The cast will help it get well."

Robert said, "The cast looks funny."

The nurse said, "It will help you get well.
And your friends can write their names on it."

Mrs. Oliver thanked the doctor and the nurse.
"Thank you for helping us quickly," she said.

The cast helped Robert get well.
The cast covered his leg.
And the names of Robert's friends covered
    the cast.

Fern Looks for Her Purse

purse (purs)	thirty

Fern Roberts is going to her job.
She has a job at a doctor's office.
Fern is a nurse.

Fern is looking for her purse.
She has thirty dollars in her purse.

Fern looks in the kitchen.
Her purse is not in the kitchen.
She looks under the bed.
Her purse is not under the bed.

Fern looks in back of the curtains.
Her purse is not in back of the curtains.
She looks under the rug.
Her purse is not under the rug.

Fern looks in her building.
Her purse is not in her building.
She looks in the street in front of her building.
Her purse is not in the street.

Then Fern's telephone rings.
Fern picks it up.
The person on the telephone says,
    "Are you Fern Roberts?"

Fern says, "Yes, I am."

The person says, "You dropped your purse
    in front of the doctor's office.
I picked up your purse.
I looked in it.
Your name and telephone number were in it.
I will bring your purse to the doctor's office."

Fern has fifty cents in the kitchen.
She gets her fifty cents and gets on the bus.
The bus stops at the doctor's office.

The person with her purse is in front of the office.
The person is a big man.
He gives the purse to Fern.
"I am happy that I helped you," he says.

Fern thanks the man.
She thinks, "Did he take my thirty dollars out
    of my purse?"

In the office, Fern looks in her purse.
Her thirty dollars is in the purse.
Fern Roberts is a very happy person!

Ann Starts Kindergarten

| kindergarten   want (wont)   shopping |

Ann Arthur is five.
Ann is going to start kindergarten.
Kindergarten is a class for little children.
Ann wants to start kindergarten.

Ann's mother is helping her.
Mrs. Arthur tells Ann her address.
She tells Ann her telephone number.
Ann says, "My name is Ann Arthur.
My address is 246 Market Street.
My telephone number is 625-5963."

Mrs. Arthur and Ann go shopping for a dress.
The dress is for Ann.
Ann wants a red dress.
She does not want a black dress.
Mrs. Arthur gets a red dress for Ann.

Then they visit their family doctor.
Their family doctor is Dr. Miller.
Dr. Miller gives some shots to Ann.
He gives a chart to Mrs. Arthur.
He says, "Ann can start kindergarten.
This chart says that Ann got her shots.
Give the chart to the kindergarten nurse."

Ann and her mother go to the kindergarten.
Ann tells the nurse, "My name is Ann Arthur.
My address is 246 Market Street.
My telephone number is 625-5963."

The nurse tells Ann, "You said that very well."

Ann's mother says, "Ann is five.
She got her shots.
This chart says that Ann got her shots."
Mrs. Arthur gives the chart to the nurse.

The kindergarten nurse says,
    "Thank you for giving Ann's chart to me.
Ann can start kindergarten."

Mrs. Arthur thanks the nurse.
She is happy that Ann is starting kindergarten.
Ann is happy that she is starting kindergarten.

A Family Works Hard

yard	covering

The Hills have a front yard and a back yard.
Their front yard is pretty.
They have grass in the front yard.
They have a big lily in the front yard.

Mr. Hill and his son Ed are in the front yard.
They are working hard.
Ed is cutting the grass.
Mr. Hill is working on the path.
He is covering the path with little rocks.

Kim and Jill are in the back yard.
Kim is working in the garden.
The Hills have a garden in the back yard.
It is a large garden.
Jill is picking apples in the back yard.
She puts the apples in a basket.
The girls are working hard in the back yard.

Mrs. Hill is working hard in the kitchen.
She cuts up the apples.
She puts them in a pan.
Then she puts apple jelly in glass jars.
Mrs. Hill has many jars of apple jelly.

The Hill family is working hard.

The Pet Shop Burns Up

started	carried (carryd)
parked	worked

The Arthurs were at the farmers' market.
The farmers' market was in the city.
Mr. and Mrs. Arthur got in their car.
Carl Arthur started the car.
The Arthurs started for their farm.
Their farm was not far from the city.

It was getting dark in the city.
Carmen Arthur looked at the city buildings.
She looked at Smith's Pet Shop.
It was Bob Smith's pet shop.
Mr. Smith was the Arthurs' friend.
He lived in the back of his pet shop.

The pet shop was burning!
Mrs. Arthur yelled, "Carl! Stop!
Stop the car quickly!
Bob Smith's pet shop is burning!"

Mr. Arthur stopped the car quickly.
He parked the car.
He parked the car not far from the pet shop.
The Arthurs jumped out of the car.

Carmen Arthur ran to a telephone.
Carl Arthur ran to the pet shop.
He heard Bob Smith yelling.
Bob Smith was yelling, "Help!"

Carl Arthur helped his friend.
He helped him get the pets out of the shop.
Mr. Arthur picked up some cats in his arms.
He carried them to the car.
Mr. Smith picked up some snakes.
They were in a big box.
He carried them to the car.

Mr. Arthur picked up some pups in his arms.
He carried them to the car.
Mr. Smith put his pet birds in a big basket.
He carried them to the car.

Mrs. Arthur ran back from the telephone.
She helped the men get the pets out of the shop.

Some men in a red truck hurried to the shop.
They ran to stop the shop from burning.
The pet shop did not stop burning.
It burned up!

Bob Smith looked at the black building.
"My pet shop burned up!" he said.
"I worked hard to get that shop.
I worked very hard."

Mrs. Arthur said, "We will help you, Bob.
You can come to the farm and live with us.
You can put your pets in our barn.
We have a large barn."

"Yes," said Mr. Arthur. "Come with us.
You can live on our farm.
You can look for a building for your pet shop.
Then you can come back to the city."

Bob Smith said, "Thank you, my friends.
Thank you for helping me."

John Buck's Will

new	sad

John Buck has a factory in New York City.
He has a shop in New York City.
He has a farm in Black River.

John lives on the farm in Black River.
He is very sick. He is not getting better.
His doctors cannot help him.

John Buck is dead.
His family is sad.
His friends are sad.
They are sad that John is dead.

Mr. Miller comes to the farm.
Mr. Miller has John's will.
He helped John write the will.

Mr. Miller says,
   "I will tell you what is in the will.
John's will tells what he gives you.
John gives the factory in New York to his son."

"He gives the shop in New York to his sister.
He gives the farm in Black River to his mother."

The family thanks Mr. Miller.

Molly's Farm

Fox	much

Molly Fox lives on a farm.
Her farm is not far from the city.
Molly works hard on the farm.
Her children help her.
Jimmy and Ann help her very much.

Molly has apples on her farm.
The apples are big and red.
Molly and her children pick the apples.

It is hot on the farm.
Molly and her children work hard.
They get very hot.
They pick twelve big baskets of apples.

Molly sells the apples.
She sells them for six dollars a basket.
Six dollars is not very much for a basket of
    big apples.

Mrs. Fisher comes to the farm.
She gets two baskets of apples.
She gives twelve dollars to Molly.
Molly thanks Mrs. Fisher.

Many persons stop at Molly's farm.
Molly sells apples to them.
She sells the twelve baskets of apples.
She gets seventy-two dollars for her twelve
    baskets of apples.

Molly gives five dollars to Ann.
She gives five dollars to Jimmy.
She says, "You helped me very much, children."

Jimmy says, "Thanks, Mother."
Ann says, "Thank you very much."

The Girl in the Well

> down

A woman is looking for her little girl.
She comes to a man.
He is getting eggs from a hen's nest.
She says, "I am looking for my little girl.
Will you help me?"

The man says, "Yes, I will.
Listen! A little girl is yelling for help!
She is at the well.
Quick, run to the well!"

The man and the woman run to the well.
The girl yells, "Help!
I am down in the well!
I cannot get out!"

The man yells, "Little girl, we will help you!"
The mother yells, "Kim, I am with this man.
We will bring you up."

The man says, "Run to the building.
Ring the bell.
My friends will come.
Bring them to the well quickly."

The woman runs to the building.
She rings the bell.
Two men run to the building.

The woman says,
     "My little girl is down in the well.
Will you help?"
The woman and the two men run quickly to
     the well.

One man says, "I will go down in the well.
I will get the little girl."

The man gets in the well.
He picks up the little girl.
His friends help him bring her up.

Kim's mother says to the men,
     "Thank you for helping us."

One man says, "We will put bricks in the well.
Little girls will not get hurt in this well."

Will Cal Come Back?

rich	fat

Cal Miller is 18.
He lives on a farm with his mother and father.

Cal tells his father, "Farm work is hard.
City living is better.
I am planning to live in the city.
I can get rich in the city."

Mr. Miller gives Cal 100 dollars.
"City living is not better," he says.
"But you can go to the city."

Cal says, "Thank you, Father."
Cal thinks, "I am rich."

Cal picks up his bag.
He gets in his car.
He starts for the big city.
It is very far from his father's farm.

Cal visits shops in the big city.
He gets many things in the shops.
He does not work.

Cal stands on the street with the men.
He watches the cars.
He watches the girls.
He gives them some of his dollars.
He does not work.

Cal looks in his bag.
He has seven dollars.
"I am not rich," he thinks.
He sells his bag.
He sells his car.
Cal does not have friends to help him.
He thinks, "City living is hard.
I will get a job."

He asks a woman in an office for a job.
She does not have a job for Cal.
He asks a man in a factory for a job.
The man does not have a job for Cal.
He asks a man in a gun shop.
"Get a farm job," the man says.
"Farmers have work."

Cal cannot get a job in the city.
He gets on a bus and starts for a farm.
He asks the farmer for work.
The farmer gives him a job.

At the farm, Cal cuts his hand.
The sun burns him.
Cal is sick, and he is not happy.

Cal does not have a friend to help him.
He thinks, "Working for Dad was better.
I will go back to my father's farm."

Then Cal starts for his father's farm.

Mr. Miller is watching for Cal.
He is looking at the valley.
Then Cal comes.
Mr. Miller runs quickly to him.
He kisses Cal.

"Cal is back, Mother!" he yells.
"Telephone Cal's friends!
Ask them to dinner!
Pick fresh apples from the garden.
Kill a fat duck.
Kill a fat hen.
Kill two fat hens!"

Mr. and Mrs. Miller have a big dinner for Cal.
His friends come to the dinner.
They say, "We are happy that you are back, Cal."

Cal stands up.
He says, "I am happy that I am back.
Thank you, Mother and Father.
Thank you, my friends."

A Visit to the Hospital

hospital (hospitul)	hurries (hurrys)

Kitty King is in the doctor's office.
Kitty's head is hot.
Her back and neck are hot.
The doctor looks at Kitty.
He asks the nurse to telephone the hospital.

The nurse telephones the hospital.
She tells Kitty,
"They will have a bed for you at the hospital."

The hospital is on York Street.
It is not far from the doctor's office.
Kitty hurries to the hospital.
It is a big hospital.
A nurse writes Kitty's name on a chart.
The nurse puts her in a hospital bed.

Jimmy Fisher visits Kitty in the hospital.
He is her boy friend.
Jimmy brings Kitty a gift.
The gift is a lily and some ferns.
Kitty says, "Thank you for the gift."
Jimmy says, "Get well quickly, Kitty."

Kitty's other friends heard that she was sick.
She gets some letters from her friends.
The letters tell her, "Get well quickly!"

Kitty is better.
She is sitting up in bed.
The doctor comes in.
He gives Kitty a checkup.
The doctor says, "You are well.
After lunch, you can pack your bag and go."

Kitty's brother comes to get her.
Her friends are happy that Kitty is well.
Kitty is happy that she is with her family and friends.

Kitty and Jimmy Are Happy

Kitty King is watching the street.
She is looking for Jimmy Fisher.
Jimmy is Kitty's boy friend.

Jimmy is coming up the street.
Kitty runs to him.
Jimmy kisses her.
Jimmy puts a box in her hand.
A pretty ring is in the box.
Jimmy puts the ring on Kitty's finger.
He says, "Will you marry me, Kitty?"

Kitty says, "Yes, I will marry you, Jimmy."

Kitty's mother and father are visiting her.
Kitty yells to them, "Mother! Dad!
Come and look at this pretty ring!"

Mr. and Mrs. King hurry in.
They look at Jimmy and Kitty.
They look at the ring.
Mother kisses Kitty.
Dad puts his hand in Jimmy's hand.

"Think of it!" Dad says.
"Our little Kitty will marry!"

"When will you marry me?" Jimmy asks Kitty.

Kitty laughs.
"I have many things to do first," she says.
"Mother and I will go shopping.
I will get a pretty dress.
Mother will give a dinner for your family.
We will send letters to our family and friends."

Mr. King puts his hand on Jimmy's arm.
"Come, son," he says.
"We will sit down and listen to our women."

Kitty runs to Jimmy.
Jimmy kisses her.
Mr. King whistles.
Mrs. King laughs.

Jimmy and Kitty are very happy.

In Love

love (luv)   breakfast (brekfust)   wanted

Kitty and Jimmy are in love.
Kitty loves Jimmy.
Jimmy loves Kitty.

Kitty and Jimmy get married.
Mr. and Mrs. Fisher live in a new building
    in the big city.
They are very happy.

Kitty gets up at seven.
Jimmy is in bed.
Kitty thinks, "I will get breakfast for Jimmy.
I will bring him breakfast in bed."

Kitty looks for a box.
"I can carry breakfast to Jimmy on this box,"
    she thinks.
Kitty puts a cup and a dish on the box.
She puts bread and butter on the box.
She puts a jar of jelly on the box.

Then Kitty starts to fix some eggs.
She puts some butter in a pan.
Then she puts the eggs in the pan.
She watches the eggs.
She does not want them to burn.

Just then, Jimmy comes into the kitchen.
Kitty jumps!
"You got up!" she says.
"I was getting breakfast for you.
I wanted to bring you breakfast in bed."

Jimmy kisses Kitty.
They kiss and kiss.

Then Kitty thinks of the eggs.
She looks at the eggs.
They are burned!

Jimmy is laughing.
"Burned eggs are OK," he says.
"I love burned eggs!"

"And I love you," Kitty says.

Jimmy and Kitty are in love.

A Truck Hits Jill's Car

locked

"Ed! Look!" yells Bob Oliver.
"A truck hit that car!"

"That is our car!" yells Ed Hill.
"And my sister has our car!
She was going shopping."

"The car is burning!" yells Ed.
"And Jill is in the car!"
Ed and Bob run quickly to the car.

"Bob, the car is locked!" yells Ed.
"I cannot get in!
Hurry! Get a brick or a rock!
We can hit the glass with it!
Jill is hurt, and she cannot help us!"

Bob brings a brick and hits the glass.
Ed gets his sister out of the car.
He puts her on the grass.
The car burns.
The truck does not burn.

The man in the truck is not hurt.
He runs to Jill.
"Help her," says Ed. "She is hurt.
Get a cop.
The cop will get her to a hospital."

The man brings two cops.
The cops bring Jill to a hospital.
The man in the truck brings Ed and Bob
    to the hospital.

The doctor and the nurse work quickly.
Jill's arm is hurt.
Her leg is cut.
Her back is burned.
The nurse gives Jill a shot.

The doctor puts stitches in Jill's leg.
He covers the burns on her back.
Then he puts her arm in a cast.

Ed and Bob are in the hospital office.
The man from the truck is with them.
The two cops come into the office.
They ask the man from the truck,
    "What happened?"

The man tells them what happened.
He says, "She passed my truck.
Then she went in front of me very quickly.
I hit the back of her car."

Dr. Fisher comes into the office.
"Ed, you can visit your sister," he says.
"She got a shot.
I covered her burns.
She has a cast on her arm.
And she has twenty stitches in her leg.
She is not very well.
But she will get well."

Ed and Bob hurry to visit Jill.
Ed kisses his sister.
Bob kisses Jill.
The boys are happy that they got Jill
    out of the car.
They are happy that Jill will get well.

A Traffic Cop

```
ticket
```

Don Oliver is a traffic cop.
He works in a big city.
Don has a big black whistle.

Don is standing at Center Street and First Street.
He tells the cars when to go.
He tells the cars when to stop.
The cars stop when Don puts up his hand.

Don watches the traffic.
He watches a big bus.

A little red car comes out of a parking lot.
It is going very fast.
It passes another car.
Don whistles at the red car.
The red car stops.
Don tells the man in the car,
    "You were going very fast.
You cannot go fast on city streets."

Don writes a traffic ticket.
He gives the ticket to the man in the red car.

A big black car is going down Center Street.
It turns left on First Street.
Don whistles at the black car.
The black car stops.
Don tells the woman in the car,
    "You cannot turn left on First Street."

Don writes another traffic ticket.
He gives the ticket to the woman in the black car.

A pink car stops in the street.
Don tells the car to go.
But it does not start.
A girl is in the car.
"My car will not start," she says.
"Is the battery dead?"

Don looks in the car.
"No, the battery is not dead," he says.
"I can fix your car quickly."
Don helps the girl start her car.
He does not give her a traffic ticket.

A little boy is coming back from kindergarten.
"I live in that big building," he tells Don.
Don stops the traffic.
He helps the little boy to his building.

A woman is running down the street.
She is running after a bus.
"I must get on that bus," she tells Don.
"I am going to work.
But the bus will not stop for me."
Don stops the bus for the woman.

Don Oliver works hard.
He helps traffic go up and down the street.
He helps many persons on the street.
Men and women do not get hurt in traffic
    when Don is on the street.
Children do not get hurt in traffic
    when he is on the street.

Word List

More Stories 2 is correlated to each lesson in *Laubach Way to Reading 2*. In the list of new words below, an asterisk indicates a variant of a word introduced in skill book 1 or 2, formed by adding or subtracting an ending. Variants formed with -s or -'s are not listed, however.

Word	Page	Lesson/Story
bad	50	9-3
breakfast	86	15-1
bus	48	9-2
* carried	70	12-3
cast	62	11-2
class	8	1-2
* coming	24	5-1
* covering	69	12-2
dead	44	8-3
did	44	8-3
* doing	38	7-3
down	76	13-3
dress	28	5-3
fat	79	14-1
fifty	30	6-2
Fox	74	13-2
front	58	10-3
* go	19	3-3
had	40	8-1
* having	11	2-1
* helped	61	11-1
hospital	82	14-2
* Hunt	24	5-1
* Hunts'	40	8-1

ESOL Vocabulary

If you are using *Laubach Way to English* to teach English to speakers of other languages, these vocabulary items will be new.

Lesson & Story	Page	Vocabulary and Suggestions
3-3	19	**thing**—Teach with a variety of known objects, as: "A dress is a thing. A book is a thing. An apple is a thing."
4-3	23	**pup tent**—This is defined in the story.
5-1	25	**look pretty**—This use of *look* should be clear from the story context.
9-1	47	**come back**—Demonstrate. In later stories, *back* is used this way several times with *come* and with other verbs, such as *go back, bring back, put back*.
10-2	56	**fix-it shop**—This use of *fix-it* as an adjective should be clear in the story context.
11-2	62	**cast**—Use the story illustration to explain. "Bob's leg is broken. The doctor put a cast on Bob's leg."
12-1	66	**kindergarten**—This is defined in the story.
12-2	69	**yard (front yard, back yard)**—Use the story illustration to explain.
13-1	73	**will**—"A person writes his will before he dies. After he dies, his family reads the will. The will tells what he gave to them."
13-3	76	**well**—Use the story illustration to explain. "We get water from a well."
14-1	78	**rich**—"He has a lot of money. He's rich."
15-1	86	**love**—Contrast with *like* in pairs of sentences: "I like ice cream. I love my husband." **in love**—The meaning of this expression should be clear from the story context.
15-2	88	**locked**—"The door is locked. I can't open it." "The car is locked. I can't open it."
15-3	91	**traffic ticket**—"Jack didn't stop at the red light. The cop gave Jack a traffic ticket."